Topics for Preschool, A Series

SPACE

Readiness Activities
for Preschool and Kindergarten

Gloria Harbin, M.A., Ph.D.
Kenn Goin, M.A., M.F.A.

CHATTERBOX PRESS
NEW YORK
1987

A note to teachers:

This book is something new! It contains 10 stories to share with your students. These little tales will help them learn important facts about space.

The book also contains activities for the different interest centers in your classroom. These activities will reinforce and extend what the youngsters learn through the stories while helping them develop the all important basic skills needed for school.

Address inquiries to: Chatterbox Press
P.O. Box 7933
FDR Station
New York, NY 10150-2411

Cover design: Elizabeth Alexander
Book design: Kenn Goin
Art: Barbara Lipp
Typesetting: Central Carolina Publishing
　　　　　　Chapel Hill, North Carolina

First published in the United States of America in 1987 by Chatterbox Press, Inc.

ISBN: 0-943129-01-X

10 9 8 7 6 5 4 3 2 1

Table of Contents

Introduction

Space has fascinated generations of children. In our own time, the development of powerful rockets and shuttles and spacecraft of all kinds has spawned "space toys" of every description, television shows, and motion pictures. It's little wonder that children learn very early about rockets and planets and the possibility of travel to worlds far different than their own.

Space is a wonderful topic for preschool. The skillful teacher can use the fascination of his or her students to create an environment where children really learn something about space as they also develop their number, language, reasoning, motor, social, and perceptual skills — all of which provide the foundation for math, reading, science, and writing readiness. You will find many opportunities in this book to help children develop these skills.

The teaching approach outlined in this book is based on the following premises:
- Preschoolers learn best through play.
- Preschoolers love stories.
- Preschoolers must be allowed to learn at their own pace.

By using *Space* with your class, you will be helping children prepare for the routines of grade school. Rather than just teaching the traditional preschool skills of matching, association, etc., in isolation, this book helps you teach these skills as children also learn about an important part of our experience — space.

Space is divided into two parts:
1. **Puppet Talk** — stories and activities for large groups.
2. **Child's Play** — activities to be used with small groups in six kinds of interest centers.

Part 1 — Puppet Talk (pages 1-42)

There are ten stories with activities to be presented in a large group setting. The learning from these stories is cumulative. Therefore, you should present the stories in order . . . approximately one story every day or every other day. If you find that the children are especially fond of a particular character or story, extend it over several days . . . adding new information on each day.

There are five important parts to each story. (See Figure 1.)

1. The lists of materials. These lists are provided in boxes: the materials you will need for the story in one box and the materials for follow-up activities in another box. Almost all materials suggested for the stories are optional; make substitutions as necessary. Many of the items needed for follow-up activities are provided in the form of worksheets and cards.

2. Suggestions for teaching. In this section, costumes, character voices, and puppets to use as you read the story are listed. Puppets normally are part of a kindergarten or nursery school learning center. Adapt the puppets you have for the ones called for in this book. Or use socks, cloth bags, sticks and styrofoam, etc., to make your own puppets. You need two robot puppets (male and female) for the stories.

3. The ideas to cover. In this section, you will find a list of the three main concepts the youngsters should learn by way of your story presentation. This list will be useful if you decide to develop your own "script" or just "tell the story" instead of reading it. It will also be useful when you wish to review the concepts covered in previous stories with the youngsters. Review is always important in learning. It is especially important in early childhood when children are learning that they can remember facts and are eager to show you what they remember.

4. The story. The story may be used as a script. You can either read it to the children or "tell" it. In either case, the story is designed to be presented through the persona of a puppet or other character. There are three keys to effective use of the stories:

Key 1. Rehearsal. Whether you read or tell the story, rehearsal is worthwhile. Have fun! Be imaginative with your voice! Be as outrageous as you want. Small children love overacting!

Key 2. Marginal Notes. Review the notes in the margin before you tell the story in class. They provide worthwhile ideas for bringing the stories alive, sparking interest, and guiding discussion.

Key 3. Discussion. Be sure to provide ample time for the children to respond during the story. Young children love to talk to puppets and other funny characters . . . and by talking, they learn.

All of the stories are written in a way that helps small children learn. They include:

a. Review — In stories 2 - 10, concepts presented in previous stories are reviewed.

b. Repetition — This technique is used in all stories to reinforce concept acquisition.

c. Questions — All stories are structured so that children can respond and take part in the tales.

5. Follow-up activities. The activities that follow each story may be used in a large or small group. They are designed to reinforce the ideas presented in the main presentation while helping children develop competence with skills such as association and matching.

Many of the activities also involve dramatic play, rea-

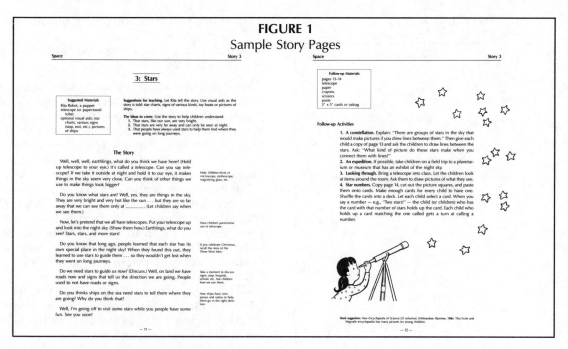

FIGURE 1
Sample Story Pages

soning, motor, and other skills. Some activities require the children to work with pages of pictures which are included with the story and may be reproduced for use in the classroom. Notice that these drawings are very simple. Most four and five year olds need visually simple pages because their visual skills are only beginning to develop in relation to printed material.

In most cases, the pages of pictures may be used either as worksheets or as cards for sorting and matching games. To enrich and deepen the children's understanding and involvement with space, supplement these drawings with others from kits and magazines.

Note: Paper-and-pencil work should be included in preschool to ready children for grade school and to help them exercise small motor, visual-perceptual, and other basic skills. However, four and five year olds need a wide variety of activities in order to grow and learn. A mix of learning approaches is the best course.

Part 2: Child's Play (pages 43-58)

There are activities for six interest centers in this section:

- dramatic play
- art
- music/movement
- science
- blocks and games
- language

Most of these activities are for small groups of children. Each activity is designed to expand the child's understanding of space and to help him or her develop specific skills — such as matching, association, and seriation. These *Focus Skills* are listed in the margin next to the activities.

Interest center decoration. The centers can be deco-

rated with pictures relevant to the areas of interest in current class work. For example, "rocket pictures" can be put up in the dramatic play center when you are working on *space travel*. The pictures should be changed as the theme of the work changes. For example, when travel is given up for *weather*, put up pictures of weather satellites, wind guages, thermometers, and so on.

Rebuses. By teaching children to recognize rebus pictures as information guides, you can develop a degree of independence in the youngsters that will be profitable for them (prereading skills) and you (more time to work with other children). For example: A card with pictures of *scissors* and an *astronaut* placed on an interest center table covered with science magazines can become a direction for the children to cut out pictures of all astronauts they find in the magazines. It takes a while to condition children to use rebuses, but the time is well spent. Try to use at least one rebus activity per week.

Making It Work!

The arrangement of the classroom contributes to the effectiveness of your teaching. If you carefully arrange interest areas and large-group spaces, children learn the daily routine more easily. They also learn where materials can be obtained without your assistance. Figure 2 (page vi) is an example of a classroom arrangement. Use the space provided below Figure 2 to sketch an ideal arrangement for your classroom. Note that your ideal arrangement will depend upon the location of the kitchen, electrical outlets, restrooms, etc. Be careful to confine activities that are messy or involve liquids to floors made of tile or other easily cleaned materials. In general, the largest space should be reserved for large-group work — such as the stories and large motor and music activities.

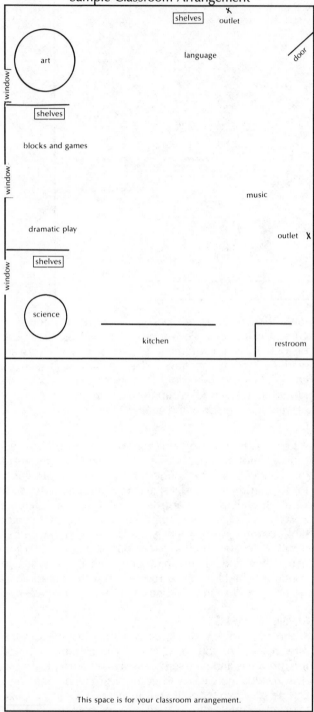

FIGURE 2
Sample Classroom Arrangement

This space is for your classroom arrangement.

1. In free-play time, you cannot disturb other groups or individual children.
2. You cannot ask the teacher questions until free play is over.

Independent work. It is also useful to assign independent work periodically. Children need this activity as preparation for grade school where there will be much less play and more work. It also allows children extra practice with tasks that are difficult for them.

Going Further

There are many ways to expand your classroom work on space. Consider creating displays with the children's help. The displays can be centered around different space topics — e.g., planets, star charts, sun, moon, etc. You can also teach the children the names of the planets, create a cardboard cutout for each planet, and have children order the planet cutouts by size.

All of these kinds of activities will help children develop skills in classification, association, matching, and seriation. Figure 3 offers ideas for putting together various bulletin board displays on space.

FIGURE 3
Bulletin Board Ideas

Planets	**Sun's Gifts**
relationship to sun	light, warmth
order and size	plant growth
Space Travel	**Stars**
kinds of spacecraft	travelers' guideposts
space traveler's	why stars shine
suitcase	

Visitors and visiting. Children love variety. When possible, ask various professionals to come to class and talk about how their professions have been affected by and have contributed to space exploration. Doctors, chemists, engineers, secretaries (computers), pilots, writers, and many others are in professions that have given significantly to — and have also been profoundly altered by — expeditions beyond earth.

A note on resources. There are many wonderful books and magazines on space. Some of the best pictures can be found in *Odyssey* magazine (1 year subscription — 12 issues — is $16. Write Odyssey Magazine, 1027 N. Seventh St., Milwaukee, WI 53233). Also look for publications of the National Air and Space Museum, the National Geographic Society, and the National Aeronautics and Space Administration.

Free play. In addition to the kinds of large- and small-group work included in this book, allow children to have free-play times. These are periods when selected children get to choose an activity to do on their own. However, for free play to be useful — i.e., a period of time when some children are occupied so that you can work with other youngsters or groups — you must establish rules:

1

Puppet Talk

This section contains 10 stories to tell or read to the children. After each story, there are follow-up activities to reinforce and extend the information contained in the stories.

1: Earth and the Universe

Suggested Materials
Rita Robot, a puppet world globe

Suggestions for teaching. Use a toy robot or a puppet. Call the robot *Rita*. Use a special "robotic" voice.

The ideas to cover. Use the story to help children understand:
1. That the earth is very big and round and heavy.
2. That we live on earth and all the people and places we know are on earth.
3. That the earth is a part of the universe.

The Story

Hi boys and girls. Look at me. Do I look like you? Of course not! I'm a robot. My name is Rita. Have you ever seen a robot before? I've come to earth from outer space to visit with you. Do you know where outer space is? (Discuss.) Yes . . . it is way up in the sky.

Where is outer space? It's up in the sky. It's any place that isn't on earth.

I have something exciting to show you. (Hold up globe.) This is called a *world globe*. This is the way the earth looked to me when I stopped on the moon for breakfast this morning — before I flew down to earth.

Ask children what they think robots eat for breakfast.

What shape is this globe? (Wait for answer.) Right, it's round. The earth is round. But the earth is much bigger than it looks here (point to globe). It is so big that you live on it and all other *people* live on it. This *room* is on earth. So is your *house*. So are the *streets* outside of it. Can you name other things on earth?

This concept may be difficult for children. The important thing for them to understand is that they live on earth.

The earth is very, very heavy and very, very big — we call it a *planet*. Can you say *planet*? I bet you didn't know that the earth is not the only planet! There are many, many planets. Some of the other planet names are Mars, Venus, and Saturn.

Help children contemplate the weight of earth by asking them to lift heavy things — e.g., a brick, a chair. Then explain that the earth is thousands and thousands of times heavier than all those things they lifted put together. No person could ever lift the whole earth.

All of these planets are very big — like earth. All of the planets are in a place called the *universe*. Can you say *universe*?

Well, I have to go to another planet in the universe for a little while. But I'll be back. (Rita waves.) Over and out!

It is enough to expose the children to the concept of universe. Answer their questions. Don't try to force understanding.

Follow-up Materials

pages 4–5
paper
crayons
scissors
paste
3" x 5" cards or oaktag

Follow-up Activities

1. Field trips. If you are fortunate enough to be close to a planetarium, arrange to take the children. They'll love looking at exhibits of the stars and planets and looking through a telescope. Another field trip idea: Go to a space museum or a museum with an exhibit on space.

2. Color my universe. Copy page 4 for each child. Ask the youngsters to color the sun *yellow*, the moon *blue*, and the stars *green*. Then ask them to use other colors for the rest of the picture. This is a good activity to use when teaching *day* and *night*.

3. Rita's portrait. Give the children paper and crayons and ask them to draw pictures of Rita. After they have completed the pictures, ask each child what Rita is doing in his or her drawing. Hang drawings around the classroom.

4. Earth shapes. Copy page 5, cut out the picture squares, and paste them onto cards. Ask children to find all the things that are the same shape as earth.

Or ask each child to draw a card in turn, tell whether or not the picture on it is of something shaped like earth, and then to pantomime for the class what we do with the item on the card.

Book suggestion: *Science on a Shoestring* by Herb Strongin (Menlo Park: Addison-Wesley, 1976). This book includes hundreds of science experiments for preschool through grade school.

Directions: Ask children to color the sun *yellow*, the moon *blue*, and the stars *green*. Then ask them to use other colors for the rest of the picture. Which picture shows a daytime scene? (See Follow-up Activity 2, page 3.)

Directions: Copy this page, cut out the picture squares, and paste them onto cards. Ask children to find things that are the same shape as earth. (See Follow-up Activity 4, page 3.)

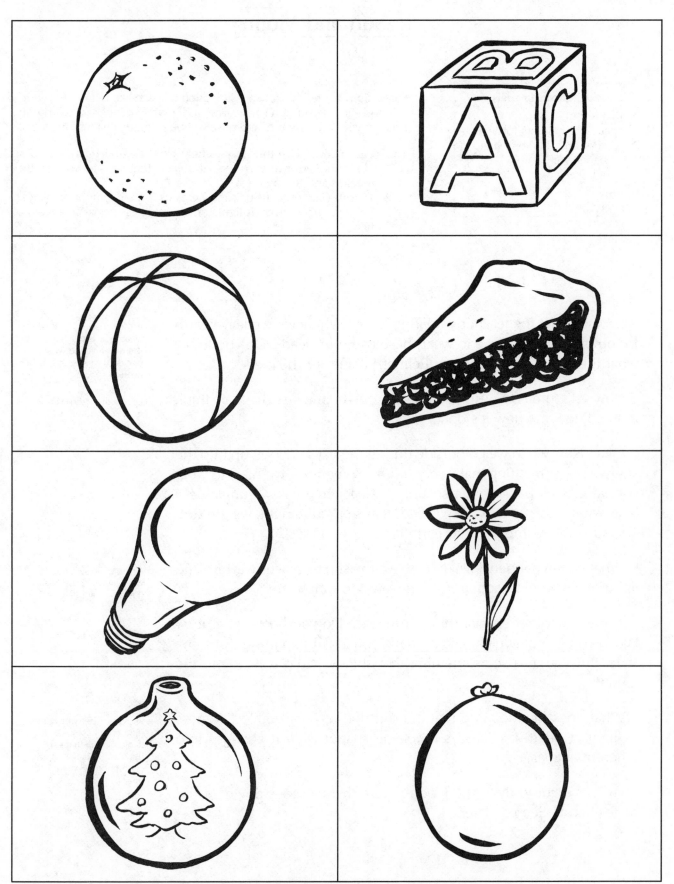

2: Sun and Moon

<table>
<tr>
<td>

Suggested Materials

Rita Robot, a puppet
space-like helmets for tea-
cher and Rita (or white
paper sacks)
sunglasses
pictures of crescent, half,
and full moons

</td>
</tr>
</table>

Suggestions for teaching. If possible, find a space-like helmet for your-self and Rita. If you don't have one, a big white-paper sack with one hole for your eyes, mouth, and nose will be just fine. Rita tells the story.

The ideas to cover. Use the story to help children understand:
1. That there are two very special objects that we see from earth: the sun and the moon.
2. That the sun gives us day and helps us in many important ways.
3. That the moon gives us light at night and has special characteris-tics.

The Story

Look at what the teacher's wearing today! Whenever we leave earth for outer space, we have to wear these over our heads. Do you know what this is called (pointing to helmet)? (Pause.) A helmet!

If they answer "You're wearing a paper bag," ask them to imagine what a person wears on his or her head in space!

Now let's pretend we're putting on our helmets so we can think better. Show me how it's done.

Let children show the mo-tions for putting on a helmet.

Okay. Now when we go outside during the day and look up into the sky, we see something that's very bright. Sometimes we have to wear special glasses because it's so bright. (Teacher puts on sunglasses.) Now what is this special thing called? (Pause.) You're right, it's the sun. The sun is very important to earth.

What would happen if we didn't have the sun to give us warmth and light? What would happen if there were too much sun?

No sun: always cold, al-ways night, no people or flowers or animals, etc.

Too much sun: sunburns, water dries up, etc.

There is another special thing in the sky. Do you know what it is? When you go out at night and it's dark, you look up in the sky and see stars. But you also see something that shines. What is it? Right, the moon!

What does the moon do that the sun doesn't? (Pause.) Yes, it gives us light at night. Is it always the same shape? (No!) It changes into different shapes.

Show pictures of moon in different phases. Or use flannelboard shapes. Or draw a full, half, and cres-cent moon on the chalk-board.

Well, I've got to fly to the moon before the sun goes down. So I'd better be off. See you later.

Follow-up Materials
encyclopedia or other
   books with picture sections on the sun and
   moon
live plant
pages 8–10
scissors
paste
4" x 6" cards or oaktag

Follow-up Activities

1. Encyclopedia. Help children find the sections on the sun and moon in a good children's encyclopedia. Let them look at the pictures and ask questions. Explain that books have many things in them that we may want to find out about.

2. Dark plant. Explain to the children that most living things need sunlight to grow and thrive. Say, "We can prove that plants need sunshine. Let's put this plant in the closet. In a week, we'll look at it again." Use a plant that requires ample sunlight — e.g., a pepperonia, coleus, or other house plant. When you remove the plant from the closet, ask children how it has changed: color, texture, etc.

3. Crescent, half, and full. Explain to the children that the moon seems to change shape from time to time. Have on display the phases of the moon. Copy page 8 for each child. Ask the children to mark the shape in each row that is one of the moon's shapes.

4. Day and night. Copy pages 9–10, cut out the picture squares, and paste them onto cards. Let each child select a card and tell whether the picture on it is for *day* or *night*. Then say, "Tell me how you know this is a daytime (or nighttime) picture."

Or copy pages 9–10 for each child. Ask them to color all the pictures of daytime things *yellow* and all the nighttime pictures *blue*.

Directions: Give each child a copy of this page. Tell them that there is a *moon shape* in each row. Ask them to find the moon shapes and color them blue. (See Follow-up Activity 3, page 7.)

Directions: Copy this page and page 10. Cut out the picture squares and paste them onto cards. Ask each child to draw a card and tell whether it has to do with daytime or nighttime. (See Follow-up Activity 4, page 7.)

Directions: Copy this page and page 9. Cut out the picture squares and paste them onto cards. Ask each child to draw a card and tell whether it has to do with daytime or nighttime. (See Follow-up Activity 4, page 7.)

3: Stars

Suggestions for teaching. Let Rita tell the story. Use visual aids as the story is told: star charts, signs of various kinds, toy boats or pictures of ships.

The ideas to cover. Use the story to help children understand:
1. That stars, like our sun, are very bright.
2. That stars are very far away and can only be seen at night.
3. That people have always used stars to help them find where they were going on long journeys.

The Story

Well, well, well, earthlings, what do you think we have here? (Hold up telescope to your eye.) It's called a *telescope*. Can you say *telescope*? If we take it outside at night and hold it to our eye, it makes things in the sky seem very close. Can you think of other things we use to make things look bigger?

Help children think of microscope, stethoscope, magnifying glass, etc.

Do you know what stars are? Well, yes, they are things in the sky. They are very bright and very hot like the sun . . . but they are so far away that we can see them only at _____. (Let children say when we see them.)

Now, let's pretend that we all have telescopes. Put your telescope up and look into the night sky. (Show them how.) Earthlings, what do you see? Stars, stars, and more stars!

Have children pantomime use of telescope.

Do you know that long ago, people learned that each star has its own special place in the night sky? When they found this out, they learned to use stars to guide them . . . so they wouldn't get lost when they went on long journeys.

If you celebrate Christmas, recall the story of the Three Wise Men.

Do we need stars to guide us now? (Discuss.) Well, on land we have roads now and signs that tell us the direction we are going. People used to not have roads or signs.

Take a moment to discuss signs: stop, hospital, school, etc. Ask children how we use them.

Do you thinks ships on the sea need stars to tell them where they are going? Why do you think that?

Now ships have compasses and radios to help them go in the right direction.

Well, I'm going off to visit some stars while you people have some fun. See you soon!

Follow-up Materials
pages 13–14
telescope
paper
crayons
scissors
paste
3" x 5" cards or oaktag

Follow-up Activities

1. A constellation. Explain: "There are groups of stars in the sky that would make pictures if you drew lines between them." Then give each child a copy of page 13 and ask the children to draw lines between the stars. Ask: "What kind of picture do these stars make when you connect them with lines?"

2. An expedition. If possible, take children on a field trip to a planetarium or museum that has an exhibit of the night sky.

3. Looking through. Bring a telescope into class. Let the children look at items around the room. Ask them to draw pictures of what they see.

4. Star numbers. Copy page 14, cut out the picture squares, and paste them onto cards. Make enough cards for every child to have one. Shuffle the cards into a deck. Let each child select a card. When you say a number — e.g., "Two stars!" — the child (or children) who has the card with that number of stars holds up the card. Each child who holds up a card matching the one called gets a turn at calling a number.

Book suggestion: *New Encyclopedia of Science* (21 volumes). (Milwaukee: Raintree, 1986). This Funk and Wagnalls encyclopedia has many pictures for young children.

Directions: Make a copy of this page for each child. Ask them to connect the stars with straight lines. Then ask them to color the picture. (See Follow-up Activity 1, page 12.)

Directions: Copy this page, cut out the picture squares, and paste them onto cards. Let each child draw a card. Ask children to count the stars on their cards. Then say a star number (e.g., "Two stars!"). The child with that card shows it and then gets to say another star number. (See Follow-up Activity 4, page 12.)

4: In Space, No Air!

Suggestions for teaching. Tell the story through Rita Robot. Have several untied, inflated balloons in hand when you begin the story.

The ideas to cover. Use the story to help children understand:

1. That there is something we breathe called *air*.
2. That we have to take air with us when we go into space.
3. That there is no air in space.

The Story

Earthlings! Watch and listen. (Hold up balloons and release them.) Do you know what was in the balloons before I let them go? Right, air. Air is what we breathe in and out every day. There is plenty of air on earth.

Take a big breath and have youngsters do the same.

But in space, there is no air. There is nothing for us to breathe. In space, people would die unless they took air with them. People who go into space wear helmets and space suits that are filled with air. The spaceship carries metal tanks that are filled with air and that can be hooked up to the spaceship.

Ask children if they can imagine what it would be like if there were no air.

When people went to the moon, there were no plants or trees or animals. Do you know why? (Pause for discussion.) Right . . . because there was no air.

Ask children what they think it is like in space. Cold or hot? Bright or dark? Wet or dry? Black and white or many colors?

Now be very quiet. Shhh! In space, it is always very quiet. Because without air, sound cannot move from place to place.

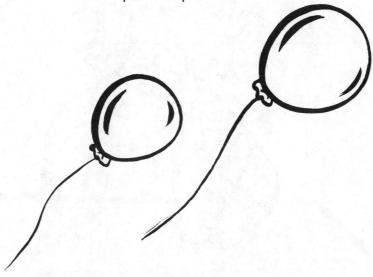

Follow-up Materials
pages 17–18
scissors
paste
3" x 5" cards or oaktag
clear plastic cups
straws
balloon

Follow-up Activities

1. Silent talk. Tell the children that we will pretend we are in space. Everyone gets a chance to "space talk." That is, they say something to someone else without vocalizing. The other person tells what was said.

2. Breathing things. Copy pages 17–18, cut out the picture squares, and paste them onto cards or oaktag. Tell the children that all living things must have air. Ask them to sort the cards into *living things* and *things that are not alive.*

3. Water bubbles. Give each child a clear plastic drinking cup and a straw. Show them how to blow bubbles in the water. (They'll already know how, most likely!) Explain that the bubbles are filled with air coming up through the water.

Or, as children watch, take an inflated, untied balloon and hold the blow hole under water. Ask the children if they know what the bubbles coming from the untied balloon are filled with.

Directions: Copy this page and page 18, cut out the picture squares, and paste onto cards. Ask children to sort the cards into *pictures of things that are alive and need air* and *pictures of things that are not alive and do not need air*. (See Follow-up Activity 2, page 16.)

Directions: Copy this page and page 17, cut out the picture squares, and paste onto cards. Ask children to sort the cards into *pictures of things that are alive and need air* and *pictures of things that are not alive and do not need air.* (See Follow-up Activity 2, page 16.)

5: Going into Space

<table>
<tr>
<td>

Suggested Materials

Rita Robot, a puppet
encyclopedia or magazines

</td>
<td>

Suggestions for teaching: Use Rita to tell the story. Have pictures about space travel on hand from an encyclopedia or magazine.

The ideas to cover: Use the story to help the children understand:
1. That it is not easy to go into space.
2. That the moon is the only place in space that people have walked.
3. That special vehicles are needed for space travel.

</td>
</tr>
</table>

The Story

Hello there, space travellers. Oops! you haven't gone into space yet, have you? Well, don't worry, lots of people haven't gone into space. In fact, very few people have ever gone into space. It's not easy to get there!

What do you think is needed to go into space? (Pause for discussion.) Well, we do need a spaceship and we need special clothes.

> Allow children to tell what they think is needed to go into space. This is a good time to review the previous story.

Do you know that the moon is the only place in space that people have actually walked? Why do you think people were able to get to the moon?

> Show encyclopedia or magazine pictures of 1969 lunar landing and related events.

To get into space, we have to build very big and very strong rockets. They have to be built out of steel and other special materials to protect the people who ride in them.

> Why were we able to get to the moon before other places? It is closer to earth than other space objects.

What do you think we use to make the rockets go? (Discuss.) Yes, it is very powerful fuel — more powerful than gasoline. It makes the rockets go very fast. Rockets fly much faster than airplanes! They have to fly very fast because it is a long way from earth to other places in space . . . such as the moon. If they didn't fly fast, the trip would take too long.

> The important idea for children to understand is that rockets need fuel just as cars and boats need gasoline.

> If children are ready, discuss *distance:* in terms of the room, in terms of the playground, etc.

Speaking of trips, I've got a spaceship to catch. It leaves the space center in half an hour. Better go. See you soon.

Follow-up Materials

encyclopedia
page 21
crayons
paste
construction paper
scissors

Follow-up Activities

1. Rocket research. Help children find the sections on spaceships and rockets in the encyclopedia. Discuss the pictures with them. "Where do the astronauts sit? Where do they put the fuel in?" Encourage children to look in other books and in magazines for pictures of rockets and other space vehicles.

2. 3-D rocket. Copy page 21 for each child. Let the children color both pieces of the rocket. Have them paste their pages onto heavy construction paper. When the glue is dry, help them cut out the rocket pieces. Cut slits as shown. Then fit the pieces together.

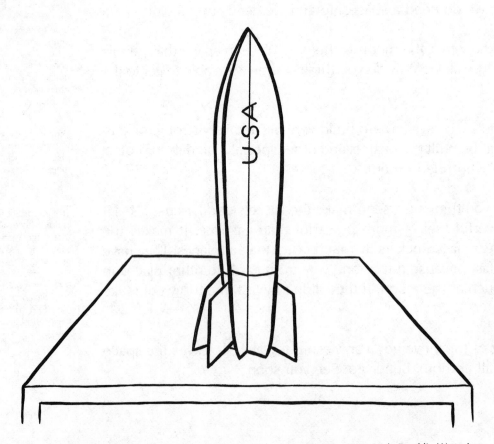

Book suggestion: *Let's Find Out About Space* by Martha and Charles Sapp (New York: Franklin Watts, Inc., 1971). This is a picture book about space.

Directions: Copy this page for each child. Let the children color both rockets and then paste the whole page onto sturdy construction paper. Help them cut out the rocket shapes and then cut slits as indicated into each rocket. Help them assemble their 3-D rockets. (See Follow-up Activity 2, page 20.)

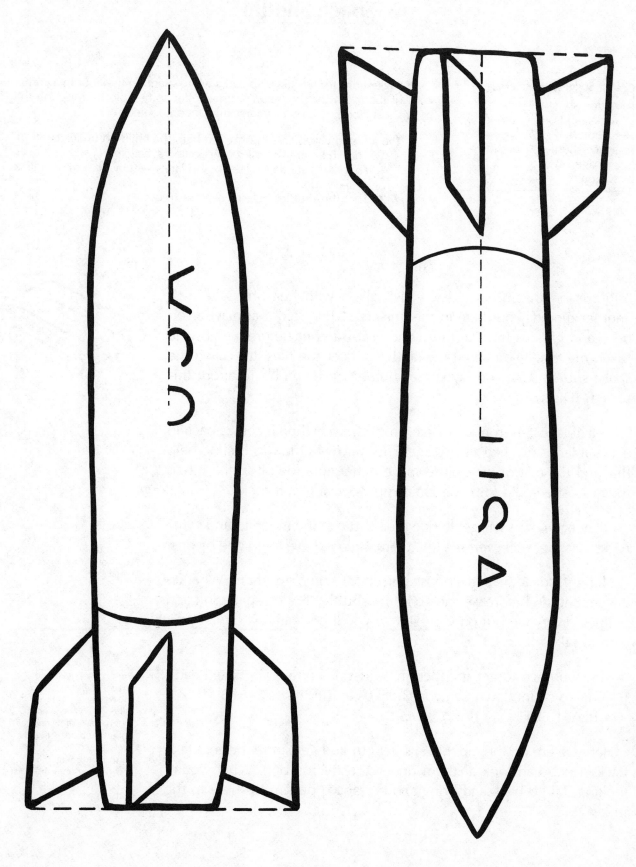

6: Space Shuttle

Suggested Materials
cotton sheet
rocks (and other "moon" objects)
space shuttle picture (or page 24)
wagon

Suggestions for teaching. Spread a white sheet on the floor in a corner of the room for the moon's surface. Put some colorful rocks on the sheet along with other interesting "moon" objects.

The ideas to cover. Use the story to help the children understand:
1. That there are special rockets called *space shuttles*.
2. That these shuttles work like airplanes — they blast off and land at space ports.
3. That the shuttles help us explore space.

The Story

Rita is on the moon today. I just talked with her. She said, "It's another nice day out here in the universe." Rita said that maybe you boys and girls would like to go and visit her. But before we go, she asked me to tell you about the kind of rocket she flies. It's called the *space shuttle*. Can you say *space shuttle*? Have you heard about this rocket? (Discuss.)

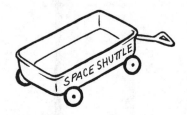

Well, it takes off from earth like a rocket. And when it comes back to earth, it lands just like an airplane. The space shuttle was built to help Rita and the rest of us explore space better. Rita took it to the moon today so she could look for some very special moon rocks.

Okay, each of us will get to ride the shuttle to the moon to find some rocks. Maybe we'll even see Rita there. But we have to go one by one.

Either use a wagon as your space shuttle or pretend that you are in a shuttle as you walk to the moon's surface.

All right, space person (choose one child), come over here. What do we need to do before we can go in the shuttle. (Put on space suit and helmet.) Everyone put on your suit so you'll be ready when it's your turn to take off.

Now we need to get strapped in — just like on an airplane. Ready. It's time to count down. Everyone help us . . . 10 - 9 - 8 - 7 - 6 - 5 - 4 - 3 - 2 - 1 - BLAST OFF!

Pretend to buckle the straps.

When everyone is on the moon, have show and tell about the objects found. Everyone comes back to earth by forming a line and holding onto the waist of the child in front. This is the space bus.

Here we are on the moon. Let's get out and get some rocks to take back so we can look at them under the microscope. While you're looking, I'll go back and bring another space person up here to the moon.

Follow-up Materials
pages 24–26
crayons
microscope
"moon" rocks, etc.
encyclopedia
scissors
paste
construction paper

Follow-up Activities

1. Space shuttle. Copy page 24 for each child. Ask children to color the windows *yellow*, the flag *red, white,* and *blue*, and the rest of the shuttle *green*. When all shuttles are completed, help children cut them out. Put them on the bulletin board or make a *shuttle-mobile* with yarn and a wire coat hanger.

2. Microscope fun. If you have a microscope, let children examine rocks under it and pretend the rocks are from other planets they have explored.

3. Encyclopedia digs. Help children find pages about space in the encyclopedia that show pictures of the shuttle and other space vehicles.

4. Matching. Copy page 25 for each child. Ask the children to use the same color for the two things that match in each row.

5. Robot march. Copy page 26 for each child. Help them cut out the picture squares. Ask the children to arrange the squares from the biggest robot shown to the smallest robot shown and glue them in that order on a sheet of construction paper. Have them color the robots.

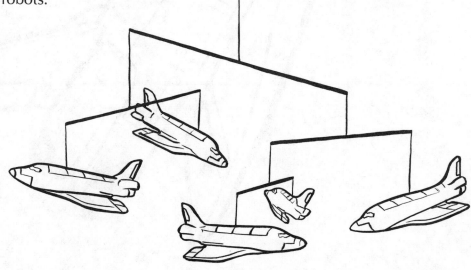

Book suggestions: *Space Shuttles* by Margaret Frishey (Chicago: Children's Press, 1982) and *The Space Shuttle Action Book* by Patrick Moore (New York: Random House, 1983). The first book has many pictures; the second book has 3-D pop-up art.

Directions: Copy this page for each child. Ask children to color the windows of the shuttle *yellow*, the flag *red, white,* and *blue,* and the rest of the shuttle *green*. (See Follow-up Activity 1, page 23.)

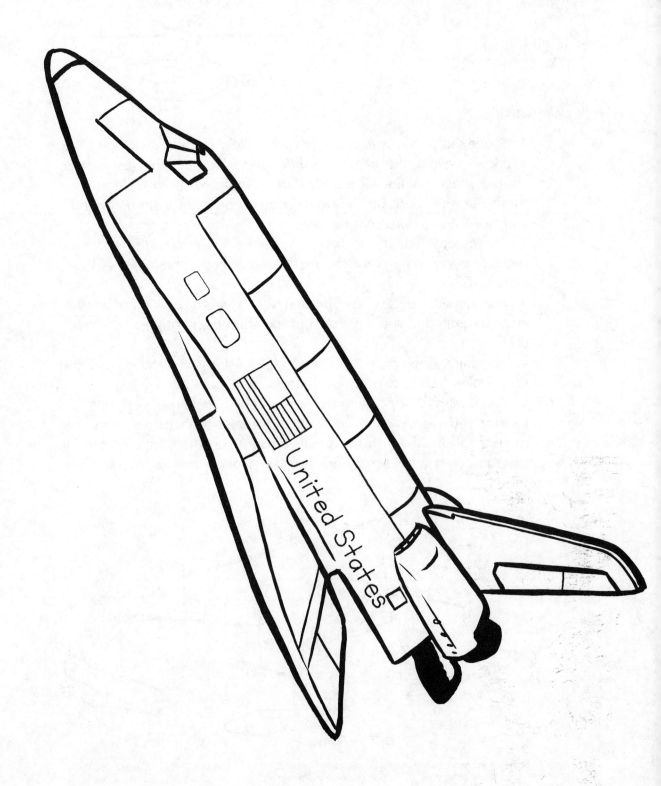

United States

Directions: Give each child a copy of this page. Ask them to find the two things in each row that are the same and color them red. Then let them use other colors for the rest of the pictures. (See Follow-up Activity 4, page 23.)

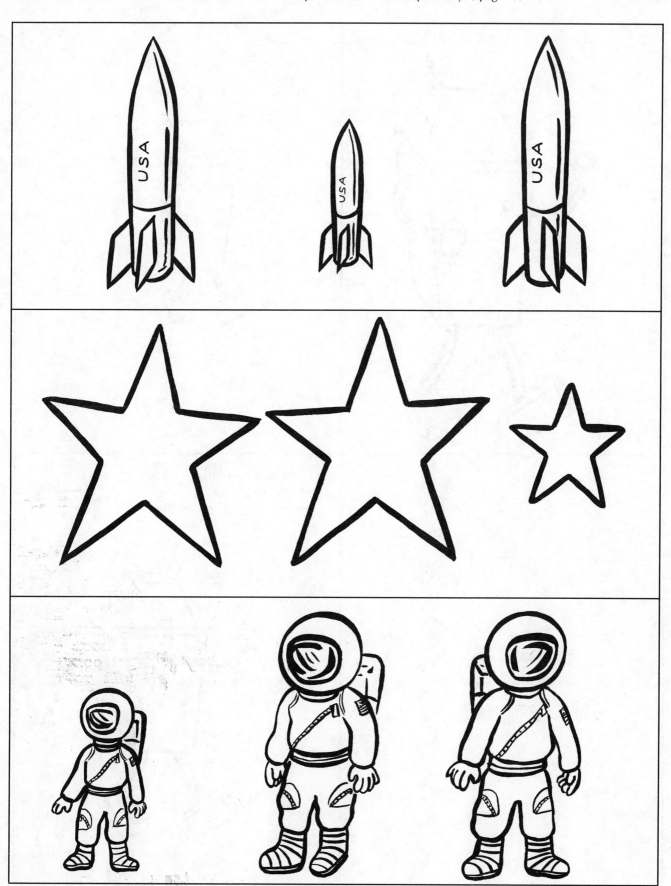

Directions: Give each child a copy of this page. Have them cut out the picture squares. Ask them to paste the squares onto a sheet of construction paper in order from the biggest robot to the smallest. (See Follow-up Activity 5, page 23.)

7: What Do We Do in Space?

<table>
<tr>
<td>

Suggested Materials

Rita Robot, a puppet
umbrella
toy airplane
world globe
pictures of satellites (from
    magazines or encyclope-
    dia)
camera

</td>
</tr>
</table>

Suggestions for teaching. Use Rita Robot to tell the story. Have an umbrella to hold over Rita's head (or your own!).

The ideas to cover. Use the story to help children understand:
1. That from space we can look down on earth and see what the weather looks like.
2. That we send up *satellites* to watch earth weather.
3. That satellites have cameras on board to take pictures.

The Story

Hello, earth friends. Do you know why I have an umbrella over my head? Because the weatherman said it is going to rain, that's why.

Do you know how the weatherman knows what the weather will be like? (Discuss.) Well, he does look at the sky and he does test the wind. But he also gets information from space.

This is a good time to introduce weather instruments: thermometer, wind guage, etc.

One of the reasons we go into space is so we'll be able to look down on earth. Have you ever been up in an airplane and looked out the window? What did you see? (Discuss.) Right, you saw clouds. What comes out of clouds? That's right! Rain and snow.

Show children how a plane flies from one place to another with the toy airplane and world globe.

We go much higher than an airplane flies when we go into space. And from our spaceship we can look down and see where the clouds are all over the world. And when the weatherman knows where the clouds are, he can figure out what the weather will be like.

Show how much farther away from the globe a space craft flies.

Now let me ask you this. Have you ever heard of a spaceship called a *satellite*? Of course you have. A satellite is a special spaceship that we send into space. It stays up there (point to sky). But we don't send people with it. The satellite sends us television pictures of what the weather is like all over earth.

Have pictures of satellites on hand to show the children.

What do you think the satellite uses to take pictures? (Pause.) Well what do you use to take pictures?

Have a camera on hand. This is a great time for a class picture!

If you went on a vacation in space, would you take a camera along? What else?

Follow-up Materials

pages 29–31
scissors
paste
4" x 6" cards or oaktag
3" x 5" cards or oaktag
styrofoam balls
toothpicks
string
thumbtacks or hooks

Follow-up Activities

1. Satellite photos. Copy page 29 enough times for every child to have one picture card. Then cut out the picture squares and paste them onto cards. Tell the children that Rita Robot has a special satellite. It sends back the pictures on the cards. Ask each child to draw a card and then tell everyone else what the satellite said the weather would be like.

2. Weather things. Use the four weather pictures from page 29: *sun, rain, snow,* and *wind*. Paste each one onto a card. Copy pages 30–31, cut out the picture squares, and paste them onto cards. Shuffle all but the four weather pictures together.

Hold up a weather picture. Let each child draw a card from the shuffled deck and say whether or not it goes with the weather picture. This game may also be played by pairs or individual children. You can expand the deck of *weather things* with pictures from magazines and kits.

3. Make satellites. Use styrofoam balls, toothpicks, foil, etc. to make satellites. Then suspend everyone's satellite (using string and thumbtacks) from the ceiling.

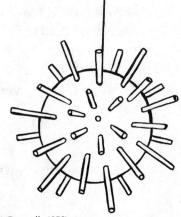

Book suggestion: *A Book of Satellites for You* by Franklin M. Branley (New York: Thomas Y. Crowell, 1958).
This book contains many illustrations to give your children ideas about the shape of satellites.

Directions: Copy this page enough times to give each child one card. Then cut out the picture squares and paste onto cards. Let children draw cards, one by one, and then tell everyone what the satellite said the weather would be like. (See Follow-up Activities 1 and 2, page 28.)

Directions: Paste the four weather cards from page 29 onto their own cards. Copy this page and page 31, cut out the picture squares, and paste them onto cards. Make a deck of all but the weather cards. *The game:* Hold up a weather card; let each child draw a card from the deck and say whether or not it goes with the weather card and why. (See Follow-up Activity 2, page 28.)

Directions: Paste the four weather cards from page 29 onto their own cards. Copy this page and page 30, cut out the picture squares, and paste them onto cards. Make a deck of all but the weather cards. *The game:* Hold up a weather card; let each child draw a card from the deck and say whether or not it goes with the weather card and why. (See Follow-up Activity 2, page 28.)

8: The Space Center

Suggested Materials

Roscoe Robot, a puppet
toy telephone

Suggestions for teaching. Use a puppet that you call Roscoe Robot to
tell the story. Open the story by having Roscoe hold a telephone
receiver to his head.

The ideas to cover. Use the story to help the children understand:
1. That there are space centers in our country.
2. That many people are needed to run a space center.
3. That a space center is an airport for rockets and other spacecraft.

The Story

Hello . . . this is Roscoe Robot calling . . . (turns to class) . . . I guess
you're wondering who I am and what I'm doing. Well, my name is
Roscoe. I'm Rita Robot's cousin. I've been trying to call her at the
astronaut's space center in Houston . . . that's in Texas. I'm supposed
to meet her down there to take a trip. But she won't answer the
phone. I guess I'll just talk to you for a few minutes . . . if it's okay?

Have you ever been to that space center? Well, it's huge . . . bigger
than an airport! There are astronauts there and many other people
too. It takes many, many people to help the astronauts get ready to
blast off.

*Tell this with great excite-
ment! Ask if children have
seen a space center on
television or at the movies.*

There are the people who fill the rocket with fuel. There are the
people who help the astronauts get in their space suits. There are the
people who built the rocket in the first place! They want to make sure
it is ready to blast off!

*Have children try to pan-
tomime filling a rocket
with fuel, putting on space
suits, etc.*

There are also doctors and nurses there. Why do you think they are
at the space center? (Discuss.) Of course, there are also cooks . . . and
let me tell you, they make some of the best hamburgers I've ever
eaten!

*Why are the doctors and
nurses present? To make
sure the astronauts are
healthy before takeoff ... to
help if an accident occurs,
etc.*

There are so many kinds of people at the space center that I can't
even remember what all of them do. Can you tell me what other kinds
of workers you think may be there?

Well, I've got to fly away to Mars today — it's one of my favorite red
planets. So I'm off to the space center for blast off with Rita. It's the
only place we can take off from. One of us will be back to see you
again soon! Bye.

*Explain that earth looks
blue from space. Ask what
color they thought it
would be? Why?*

Follow-up Materials
page 34
scissors
3" x 5" cards or oaktag
paste

Follow-up Activities

1. Space travel match. Copy page 34, cut out the picture squares, and paste them onto cards. Have the children sort them into things they think have to do with space travel and things that do not. Or let each child draw a card, in turn, and hold it up. The children say whether they think it has to do with space travel or not.

2. NASA ground control. Have half of the children pretend to be rockets. They are to jump as high into the air as they can when the other half of the children reach the number 5 while counting in unison with your assistance. Reverse positions after first launch.

For another auditory discrimination game, tell the children to jump every time they hear you say a certain word or phrase: for example, "Moon Man." Then, make up a story around the word or phrase. For example, "It was a long time ago when the *Moon Man* first appeared. He had a long beard . . . as white as snow. The *Moon Man* had a face with a bright white smile . . . etc."

Directions: Copy this page, cut out the picture squares, and paste them onto cards. Have children sort cards into *things that have to do with space travel* and *things that do not have to do with space travel*. (See Follow-up Activity 1, page 33.)

9: Astronauts

Suggested Materials
Roscoe Robot, a puppet

Suggestions for teaching. Use Roscoe to tell the story.

The ideas to cover. Use the story to help the children understand:
1. That astronauts are the people who ride the spaceships into space.
2. That astronauts must be very healthy and train to go into space.
3. That astronauts can leave the spaceship only for a limited time . . . because space is not like earth.

The Story

Earthlings, gather round and help me count down: 10 - 9 - 8 - 7 - 6 - 5 - 4 - 3 - 2 - 1 - BLAST OFF! That was fun! Let's do it again: 10 - 9 - 8 - 7 - 6 - 5 - 4 - 3 - 2 - 1 - BLAST OFF! Who do you think blasts off in spaceships?

Hold up fingers as you count down.

Let youngsters tell you who they think blasts off: they do, pilots do, animals do, etc.

Let's talk about astronauts today. Does anyone remember what astronauts do? (Discuss.) Right . . . they fly spaceships through space.

Can anyone be an astronaut? (Discuss.) I have a sister, Sheila Robot, and she is an astronaut. She is very brave and she's very strong and healthy.

The people who want to be astronauts have to build up their bodies by eating good kinds of food. They also need to run and ride bicycles and do other kinds of exercises. They do all these things so they can breathe better. There is no air in space. Remember? They have to breathe through their space suits!

Ask: "What kinds of food do you think astronauts eat?"

Ask: "What other exercises do astronauts do?" Have several children show how these exercises are done.

And even though they try to get very strong and healthy, they still have to wear their space suits most of the time. They still cannot go very far from their spaceships when they are in space. And they can never walk in space without their space suits. Why do you think that is?

Well, I've got to be on my way to the Milky Way. That's where I live. I'll see you back here on old mother earth again soon! Bye.

Roscoe waves goodbye to class.

| **Follow-up Materials** |
| pages 37–38 |
| paste |
| oaktag or construction |
| paper |
| scissors |
| tape |
| crayons |

Follow-up Activities

1. Apollo puzzle. Copy the rocket on page 37, paste it onto oaktag or construction paper, and cut it out. Explain to the children that these pieces are parts of the rocket that went to the moon. Have the children practice putting the parts together in the right order by matching the numbers.

Or, make a copy of page 37 for each child. Have them cut out the pieces, put the rockets together with tape, and put their names on their rockets. Help them as necessary. Line up everyone's rocket on the wall or board . . . ready for takeoff.

2. Astronaut count. Pass out copies of page 38. Ask the children to find as many astronauts as they can in the rocket. Have them write the number of astronauts they found in the number box if they are working on numbers. Then let them color their rockets and astronauts.

Book suggestion: *You Will Go to the Moon* by Mae and Ira Freeman (New York: Random House, 1971). This is a storybook about a child's trip to the moon.

Directions: Copy this page, paste onto oaktag, and cut out the rocket stages. Have children show how it goes together by matching the numbers along the lines. (See Follow-up Activity 1, page 36.)

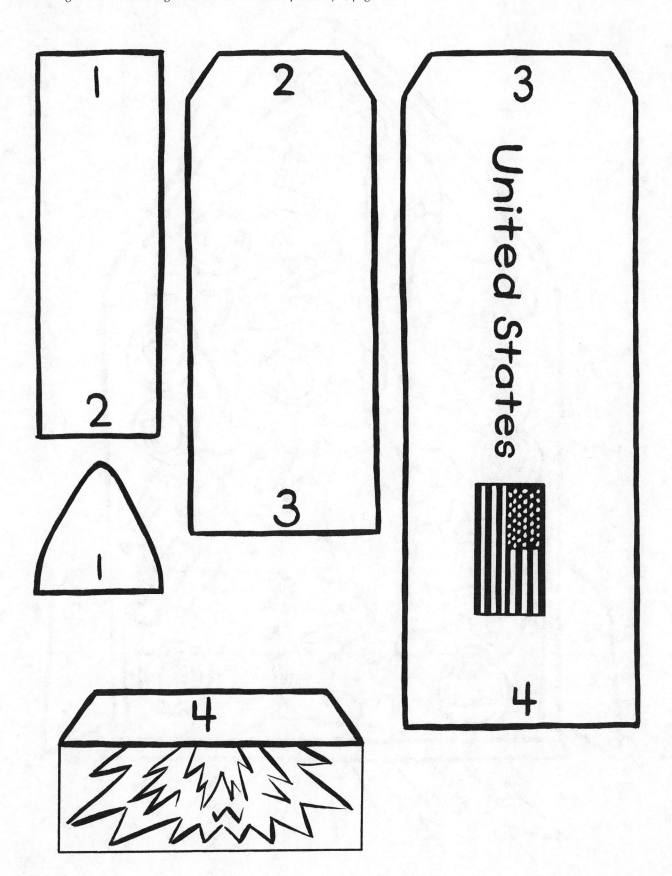

Directions: Give each child a copy of this page. Ask them to color all the astronauts they can find. Then tell them to write the number of astronauts they found in the Number Box. (See Follow-up Activity 2, page 36.)

Number Box

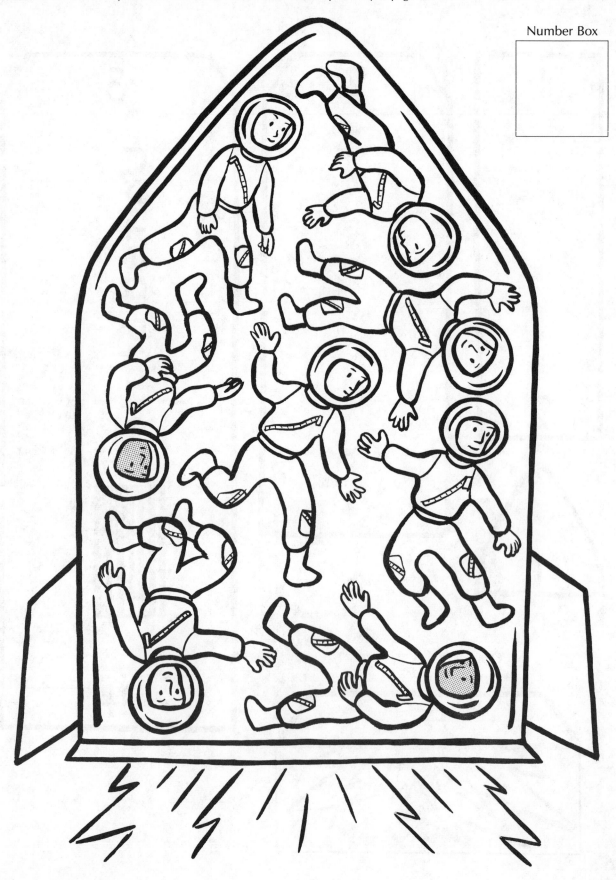

10: Space in Our Future

Suggested Materials
Roscoe Robot, a puppet

Suggestions for teaching. Use Roscoe Robot to tell the story.

The ideas to cover. Use the story to help children understand:
1. That men and women plan to continue exploring space.
2. That space stations allow spaceships to go far into space.
3. That some things we have discovered by going into space have helped us on earth.

The Story

Well earth friends, this is my last day with you. Tomorrow, I will ride my rocket back into space. But, of course, I'll come back to visit with you . . . you are my friends.

But before I go, I wanted to ask you if you are interested in going into space? Do you know that people all over the world want to keep going farther and farther into space? Why do you think they want to go?

Discuss children's interests in space. Why do they want or not want to go into space.

Now we are building *space stations*. They will help us go farther into space. These stations are like airports that float in the sky. We built them so that rockets — which are like really fast airplanes — will have a place to stop and get more fuel when they are flying through space. We also built them so astronauts will have a place to pick up more food and fix their rockets if they break.

Discuss children's experiences with airports. Why do people need airports? Do we use the same things to build airports and space stations?

Ask children if they can make the sound a broken rocket makes?

Space stations also let us look more closely at the sun, the moon, and the stars. That's because they are closer to these things. There are no mountains or sunlight or earth noises in space . . . so astronauts can watch the sun and moon better from a space station.

Do you know that by going into space, we also learn things that help us on earth? When people built the first rockets, they learned how to make better computers. Can you believe that? Now we use those computers for other things. Can you think of some of the things we use computers to do?

What can computers do? Add, subtract, solve problems, play games, communicate. Can computers think? How are they like people? How are they different?

Well, I've got a rocket to catch. Will you earthlings help me count down for take off? Okay . . . here we go . . . 5 - 4 - 3 - 2 - 1 BLAST OFF! See you earth people next time I land!

Follow-up Materials
pages 41–42
scissors
paste
3" x 5" cards or oaktag
paper
crayons

Follow-up Activities

1. **Planet cross out.** Give each child a copy of page 41. Have them cross out the planets in each row that are the same. Then have them color the planets that are different.

2. **Space rain.** Copy page 42, cut out the picture squares, and paste them onto cards or oaktag. Then explain to the children that it does not rain in space. Rain is a special thing we have here on earth.

Have the children sort out all the cards that show things that could not be in space because there is no rain.

Or make enough cards so each child can draw one. Ask the child whether he or she thinks the picture on the card could be in space. Ask the child to explain.

3. **Draw-a-station.** Give children paper and crayons. Ask them to draw a space station. Suggest that they draw in rockets and astronauts. (Artistic merit is not required or expected!)

Magazine suggestion: *World*, from National Geographic, has many stories on space. A one-year subscription (12 issues) is $10.95. Write: World, Dept. 00787, 17th & M Streets, NW, Washington, DC 20036.

Directions: Give each child a copy of this page and have the children cross out the planets in each row that are the same. (See Follow-up Activity 1, page 40.)

Directions: Copy this page, paste it onto oaktag, and cut out the picture squares. Have children sort the squares into two groups: *things that need rain and therefore can't be in space* and *things that do not need rain and can be in space.* (See Follow-up Activity 2, page 40.)

2
Child's Play

The activities in this section are for the following interest centers:

- dramatic play
- art
- music/movement
- science
- blocks and games
- language

While children should be given ample time for free play and other self-directed activities in these areas, the teacher may also want to use the specific activities that follow with small groups or individuals. These activities will reinforce and extend the learning that takes place through the large-group activities of section 1.

Dramatic Play Center

What We Do

You need: scissors
        magazine pictures of day and night scenes
        cards or oaktag
        paste
        envelope

Cut pictures from magazines that show people in various daytime and night-time activities:

Day	*Night*
breakfast	reading a book in bed
playing ball	lighting a candle
swimming	dressing for bed
getting dressed for school	getting ready to go to bed

Put the pictures in an envelope. When children play together, one child can draw a picture and — without showing it to the others — act out the scene while his or her companions try to guess what scene it is.

If you are working with the children, you can suggest scenarios without using pictures. For example, "Tommy, show me how you get ready to go to bed at night."

In the beginning, it will be helpful for an adult to be on hand to guide this kind of activity and to encourage children to play cooperatively. When children seem confused by a picture or a suggested scenario, ask "What happens next? (or first?)" before giving any suggestions.

Weather Clothes

You need: weather clothes and props (e.g., sunglasses, short-sleeved shirts, summer hats, sandles; raincoats, umbrellas, rain boots; coats, winter caps, mittens, snow boots)

If you do not have one already, make a *weather box.* This is simply a big box with lots of different kinds of clothes in it. Have on hand some or all of the weather clothes listed in the *You need* list above. Adult or over-sized clothing is often better than children's clothes — it is easier for children to get on and off, and the children often prefer big people's clothes to their own.

Have the children pretend they are at home and getting ready to dress to go outside. Have one child choose a kind of weather (snow, rain, sunshine, etc.) or have weather cards available (see page 29) for them to select from. After a weather choice is made, the children decide what clothes they will need for it. They choose the clothes from the weather box and dress up. Sometimes encourage children to dress independently. Other times, encourage children to help each other. Dressing will give children practice with a wide variety of fasteners.

Focus Skills
cooperative play
day and *night*
association

Focus Skills
cooperative play
association
independent play
small motor

Space Work

You need: hats (different kinds for different jobs — e.g., nurse, doctor, painter, construction worker, etc.)
job tools (e.g., paint brush, play computer, safety glasses, etc.)
box

Collect a number of job hats and tools and put them in a box. When children first play this game, provide as much guidance as they need.

First, let each child choose a hat or tool. Then provide a scenario: "We are going to be launching a rocket to Venus today. We need many workers to help our astronauts get ready. . . . I see you workers have on your hats and some of you have tools." Encourage children to talk about the jobs their hats or tools represent. For example, "Sally, I see you're wearing a painter's hat. What kinds of things do you paint at the space center? Can you show me how you paint them?" Or, "Tom, you have a computer. What kinds of things do you use it for in your space job? Can you show me how it works?"

After children have gone through this activity once, encourage them from time to time to play Space Work on their own.

Focus Skills
cooperative play
expression
association
jobs

Lunch for Space

You need: play food
lunch pail

Have children work in pairs. Tell the children to pretend they are astronauts preparing for take off, and they are packing each other's lunches. Encourage them to discuss the kinds of food they need to take. Let each child tell the packer what his or her favorite food is and why it's important to take that food into space. (If you have a chart of foods in the four major food groups — vegetables and fruit, dairy foods, grains, and proteins — this activity can be helpful in teaching children about balanced meals.)

Focus Skills
cooperative play
health

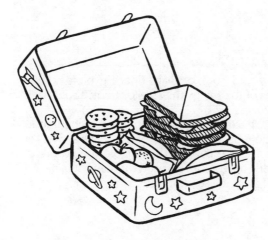

Art Center

Space Sponges

You need: sponges
scissors
paint
paper

Focus Skills
small motor
seriation
imagination
vocabulary: *big, little,
largest, smallest, in
between*

Cut different-sized rocket shapes out of the sponges. Have children dip the shapes into tins of tempera paint and make rocket shapes on paper. Vary the activity as follows —
1. Have children print the rockets in order from largest to smallest.
2. Have them make three big rockets on one side of a page and three little rockets on the other side.
3. Have the children print one or two rockets on a page and then finish the page by drawing stars, the moon, earth, astronauts, etc.

This activity can be done on tables or at easels.

The Rocket Touch

You need: construction paper
crayons
yarn
scissors
other tactile materials (ric rac, toothpicks, ice cream sticks, etc.)
paste

Ask children to draw a big rocket on a piece of paper. Or copy page 21 and give each child one of the rocket shapes; have them paste the shapes onto pieces of construction paper.

Then let children use yarn or other materials that can be pasted over the outlines of the rocket. Encourage children to discuss size, shape, feel of material, color, etc.

Space Log Covers

You need: construction paper
colored markers
paste
glitter
stapler
white paper

Explain to children that a *log* is a record book or diary. Space explorers keep logs to write about or draw pictures of the things they see or think about each day they are in space.

Give each child a piece of 8½" x 11" construction paper. Ask the children to draw a star or sun or moon on their covers. Or, simply ask for a space scene. Let children use paste and glitter to finish the covers. Then staple the covers to several sheets of white writing paper. The logs can be used for many activities: a book of day/night pictures, a book of space scenes, etc.

Robot Puppets

You need: copies of page 26
crayons
tongue depressors
paste
paper bags (optional)
sequins (optional)

Focus Skills
small motor
cooperative play
language development

Give each child a robot square from page 26. Let them color the robots and squares. Have each child paste his or her square onto a tongue depressor. The children can have their robots talk to each other or act out stories in the language arts center.

Robot puppets can also be made out of paper bags on which children have drawn eyes, noses, and mouths. The features can be filled in with sequins.

Space Delicacies

You need: modeling dough (salt or flour dough)
[flour dough recipe: 4 cups flour, ¼ cup salt, 1½ cups water, 1 table-spoon oil, food coloring as desired]

Focus Skills
small motor
creativity
cooperative play

Tell the children that you want them to make astronaut foods out of the dough. Encourage children to make foods that everyone knows as well as special foods that are available only in space. Encourage children to name the new food shapes . . . but to resist the temptation to eat them.

Music/Movement Center

People Rockets

You need: pointed birthday party hats

Have all children put on the pointed hats. Tell the children that they are now rockets. The point at the top of their heads is the rocket's nose. Then give each rocket a destination (a point across the room). Have them one by one show how their rockets move. After each rocket reaches its destination, help the children describe the movement: fast or slow, straight or zigzag, high or low. To add to the fun, countdown before each rocket blasts off.

Focus Skills
large motor
following directions
imagination
vocabulary: *fast, slow, straight, zigzag, high, low*

Singin' in Space

You need: paper
pencils
cassette recorder (optional)
cassette (optional)

Tell children to imagine they are going into space for a long, long time. While they are away, they'll want to make up songs to entertain themselves and their fellow astronauts. Teach them this short lyric to the tune of "London Bridge":

> Oh, the astronaut is very brave,
> very brave, very brave.
> Oh, the astronaut is very brave —
> way out in space.

Then let the youngsters help you make up other songs. The stars, moon, and sun are all good topics. "Ring-around-the Rosie," "Bluebird," and "Pop Goes the Weasel" are all easy melodies. Record the lyrics so children can play them in the interest center and then copy them for children to take home.

Focus Skills
creativity
following directions
rhythm

Day and Night Songs

You need: songbooks (optional)
prerecorded cassettes or records (optional)
cassette recorder
blank cassette tapes

There are many songs with topics related either to *day* or *night*. Sing or play these songs to the children. Ask the following about each song: "Does it have to do with day or night? How do you know?"

Then record individual children singing various songs. When the tape is played back, have children guess who was singing and whether the song was a day or night song.

Song suggestions: "Twinkle, Twinkle, Little Star," "This Is the Way We Wash Our Clothes . . . ," "Moon River," and various Christmas carols.

Focus Skills
thinking
auditory discrimination

Rocket Sound

You need: musical instruments
cassette recorder
blank cassette tapes

Ask each child, in turn, to make the sound of a rocket blasting off. Then let everyone choose an instrument. Now have children, in turn, use the instrument to make the sound of a rocket blasting off.

Focus Skills
small motor
imagination
following directions
auditory discrimination

Then explain to the children that you're going to make a tape of the rockets blasting off. When you point to each child, he or she is to make the sound of the rocket first with his or her voice and then with the instrument. After everyone is on the tape, play it back and let children guess who made each sound. (If possible, obtain a tape of a rocket blasting off for children to compare with their own tapes.)

Moon Music

You need: bottles, glasses, spoons, books, and other potential sound-makers
cassette recorder (optional)
blank cassette tapes (optional)

Focus Skills
imagination
cooperative play
small motor

Tell the children, "We're going to put together a moon band. On the moon, there are no musical instruments . . . so we'll have to find other things to make music with." Anything in the classroom is okay to use: jars, bottles, sticks, rocks, books, marbles, beanbags, etc. Let each child find (or select) an instrument. Have each child first play his or her instrument choice alone. Then let everyone play together. Record the moon band's hits!

Science Center

One-Month Weather Board

You need: 4 pieces of white construction paper
posterboard
colored markers
white paper (optional)

On each piece of construction paper, draw one of the following weather symbols:

sun   rain   clouds   snow

Teach these symbols to the children. Then prepare the posterboard by drawing the current month's calendar on it.

Each day, discuss the weather with the children. Then help one child draw the appropriate symbol in the day's square on the calendar. (Or, copy these symbols several times and cut them out.) Encourage children to use several colors for their symbols.

As a variation, have each child keep an individual weather board on an 8½" x 11" sheet. These sheets can be posted in the science center.

Temperature

You need: thermometer (indoor/outdoor)
posterboard
marker

Space is an excellent topic through which to teach the concept of temperature. Install the thermometer in a place where children can check it easily. Teach them how to read the position of the mercury.

Draw the current month's calendar on the board. Each day, discuss the temperature and record the indoor and outdoor readings in the appropriate calendar box. Other concepts to introduce in regard to temperature:
1. **Space temperatures** — In space, it is very cold . . . much colder than the freezer in the refrigerator.
2. **Sun temperatures** — The sun is much hotter than any fire on earth.
3. **Water temperatures** — Water can be very hot, warm, cold, or frozen.
4. **Body temperatures** — People's bodies are always the same temperature unless they are sick . . . then they have a *fever*.

Magnification

You need: telescope
microscope
reading glass
paper
pencils

Have available as many magnifiers as possible. Encourage children to look at various materials through each magnifier. Discuss how some of the tools are used to help us explore and understand space. Telescopes help us look more closely at things in the sky. Microscopes help us take a closer look at rocks and other things that we bring back from space or find here on earth. Magnifying or reading glasses help us in the same way. Let children draw what they see when they look through these magnifiers.

Space Rocks

You need: rocks
paper
pencils or crayons
water
soda water

Focus Skills
observation
small motor
vocabulary: *shape, size, color, hard, soft, sharp, smooth, crack, chip*

Explain to children that many planets are made up of rocks and that there are many kinds of rocks. Have available a variety of rocks or let children gather rocks from the playground. Then let the youngsters draw pictures of several of the rocks. Call their attention to *shape, size,* and *color.* Are the rocks *hard* or *soft? Sharp* or *smooth?*

Then explain that rocks can be changed. If they are hit or dropped, they can *crack* or *chip.* If liquids are poured on them, they can look different. Let children try putting water on some of the rocks and soda water on others. What changes occur?

Sun Shine Bright

You need: 3 drinking glasses
water
food coloring
medicine droppers
paper, various kinds

Focus Skills
thinking
observation
vocabulary: *evaporation*

Help the children explore one of the sun's effects on earth — evaporation. Explain that the sun's light brings heat to earth. Discuss the effects of this heat: sunburns, plant growth, seasons, drying of clothes, etc.

Then do an experiment. Have three glasses of water available. Color the water in each glass by adding a few drops of food coloring.

Let children use medicine droppers to put the same amount of water on various kinds of paper: paper towel, white or buff construction paper, tissue paper, etc. Have them set some of the paper in sunlight and some in a closet or pantry. Check the paper every 5 minutes. Which paper *dried* faster? Where did the water go? It went into the air! When water dries up, it goes into the air, and that process is called evaporation.

Blocks and Games Center

Design Engineer

You need: drafting paper or plain paper
pencils or crayons
optional: oaktag, paste, scissors, copy of page 21

Explain to the children that people who plan the rockets and spaceships first draw the way they want the ships to look on paper. These people are called *engineers*.

Tell the children that they can be engineers. Ask them to use the paper and pencils to draw plans for rockets.

If children are not yet able to work on this kind of task, copy page 21, paste it onto oaktag, and cut out one of the rockets. Let some children trace around the cut-out rocket; let others use the oaktag from which it was cut as a template to outline a rocket. For other children, you can use the template to make a dot-to-dot rocket.

Focus Skills
vocabulary: *engineer*
imagination
small motor

Building Spaceships

You need: picture of spaceship
boxes of various sizes (large)
large blocks
optional: foil, helmets

Hang a large picture of a spaceship or rocket in the block center. (You can redraw one from this book on a large sheet of paper or, better yet, find a large photograph of one in color.) Then tell the children to examine it closely. Explain that you want them to build a rocket like the one in the picture so they will be able to take a ride into space.

Then help children build the spaceship with boxes and blocks. As they build, encourage them to look at the picture for guidance. The rocket must be large enough to seat two.

Once the spaceship is built, let children take turns as astronauts who are blasting off to various exotic space destinations. When each pair of children returns, ask them what they saw on their trip and where they went. Did they visit any planets? To make the ride more fun, give them foil-covered helmets to wear.

Focus Skills
imagination
large motor
small motor
cooperative play
dramatic play

Space Station

You need: blocks/boxes/cylinders, etc.
wagon
foil
supplies (food, etc.)

Use this activity to help children understand the idea of a *space station*. Explain that you want to build a space station. (Note: build the space station across the room from the spaceship.) "You will use the station as a place the spaceship can stop for supplies when it goes on *missions*."

First, let children decide where the station will be positioned — on the moon, on a distant planet (Mars, Venus, Pluto, etc.) or floating in space. Then begin to build the station using blocks and boxes and foil-wrapped cylinders to connect parts.

When the space station is in place, astronauts can leave their "spaceship" and *shuttle* over to the station in a wagon. Have various *supplies* on board the

Focus Skills
imagination
cooperative play
small motor
large motor
vocabulary: *space station,
mission, shuttle,
supplies*

station so the astronauts can take them back to their ship. Supplies can include food (real or play), fuel (blocks, plastic containers of water, etc.), and building materials (blocks, rods, etc.).

Tabletop Dramas

You need: interlocking blocks
robots
gobots

Children can be encouraged to build other space vehicles using interlocking blocks at a table. They can use toy rockets, robots, and gobots to enhance the activity.

Focus Skills
imagination
small motor

Puzzles

You need: copies of space pictures
paste
oaktag
scissors
envelopes

Choose pictures from this and other books that show space objects or scenes. Paste these pictures onto oaktag or cardboard. (If children in your class are at many different levels in their perceptual skills, make several copies of each scene so you can create puzzles of varying difficulty.) Then cut the pictures into pieces. Vary the pieces for each puzzle (no less than three or more than nine pieces). Make the cuts all the way across the page. Store each puzzle in its own envelope.

Focus Skills
visual perception
small motor

Space Patterns

You need: copies of pages 54–56
scissors
oaktag
paste

Copy page 54, paste it onto oaktag and cut out the cards. Copy pages 55–56 and paste each page onto oaktag.

The first time children attempt this activity, help them through it. Explain that each row on pages 55–56 shows a pattern: for example, 3 rockets, 2 spacesuits, etc. The goal is to find one of the small cards to complete the pattern.

Once children understand the activity, they can play alone or in pairs. If you copy the "cards" (page 54) several times, they can use the deck of cards to make patterns. Five of the cards on page 54 are not needed for pages 55–56.

Focus Skills
visual skills
reasoning
sequencing

Directions: Copy this page, paste it onto oaktag, and cut apart the 15 picture squares. Use these squares with the pattern boards on pages 55–56. (See *Space Patterns*, page 53.)

Directions: Copy this page and page 56. Have children find the square from page 54 that completes each row. (See *Space Patterns*, page 53.)

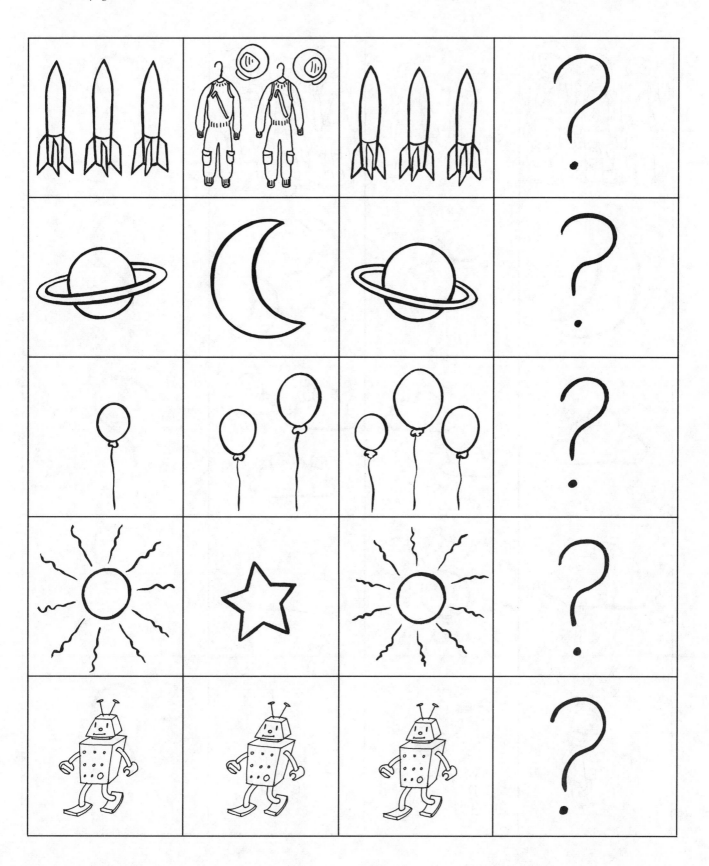

Directions: Copy this page and page 55. Have children find the square from page 54 that completes each row. (See *Space Patterns*, page 53.)

Language Center

Flannel Fantasy

You need: flannel board
scissors
glue
oaktag
flannel
patterns from this book

Tell one of the stories from the first section of this book at the flannel board. Some of the pictures you may need for the stories include: rocket, robot, stars, moon, sun, space station, and space shuttle. Copy as many of these pictues as you need. Cut them out and glue them onto oaktag. Glue a flannel piece to the back of each cutout.

After you have told the story, let the children have turns retelling parts of the story and moving the pieces around. In the language center, have children work in pairs retelling the stories to each other using the flannel-backed pieces.

Stories

You need: cassette player
blank cassette

Have a blank tape ready to record. Then explain to the children that everyone is going to tell their own space story.

Start them off with a lead-in, such as: "There once was an astronaut named Jenny. She was just sitting down to breakfast in her spaceship's kitchen . . ." Then ask one of the children what happened next. Give several youngsters a chance to add to the story, and then finish it for them. For example, "So Jenny had a good breakfast of oranges and milk and toast and was ready to begin her work on the moon." When children are ready, allow them to come up with their own lead-ins.

In the language center, children can replay these stories. They can also work together to create new tales (with the cassette player) which they will be anxious for you to hear.

Space Objects

You need: chart paper
crayons
copies of page 58

Before the children are in the language center, write the following code on a piece of chart paper and put it on display. (For the swatches of color, either use colored construction paper or crayons.)

B = swatch of blue color
P = swatch of pink color
R = swatch of red color

Give each child a copy of page 58. Explain that there is a special picture on the page. To find it, the children must use the letter/color code on the chart.

Directions: Copy this page for each child. Have children color as follows: B = blue, P = pink, R = red. (See *Space Objects* on page 57.)